A Helping Hand

MPress books

A HELPING HAND

First published in 2017 by M*Press* Books

MPress Books Limited Reg. No 6379441 is a company registered in Great Britain
Tall Grass Productions is an imprint of MPress Books Limited
www.mpressbooks.co.uk

British Library Cataloguing in Publication Data
A catalogue record for this book is available from the British Library.

ISBN

978-1-9997334-0-7

Typeset in Two Fingers Bodoni
Origination by Core Creative, Yeovil 01935 477453

A Helping Hand

This book belongs to...

_____

Illustrated by Maria Floyd
Written by Clare Luther

Bounding this way and that,
both on dunes and the flat,
leapt a sporty and fit antelope.

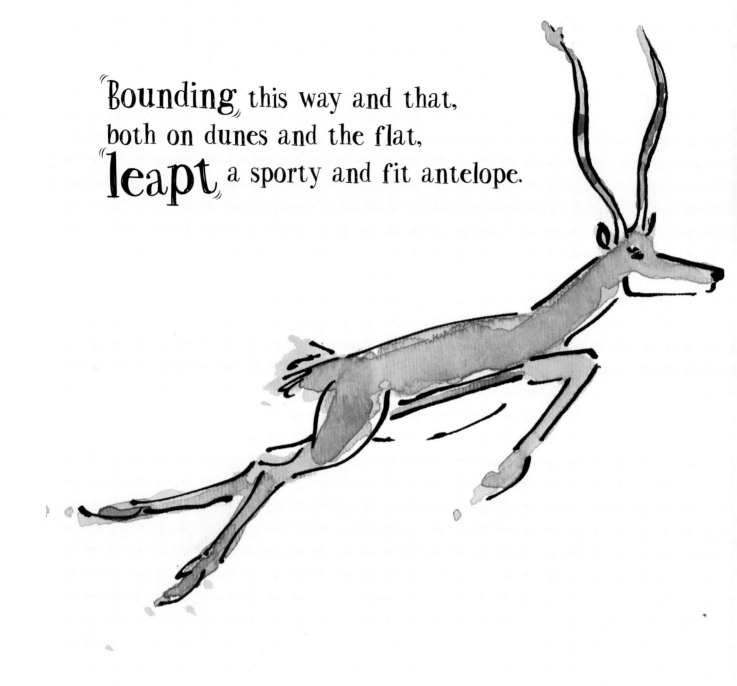

Her even-toed hooves helped this fast mammal move,
up and down all the steep sandy slopes.

This doe would rush ROUND
hardly touching the GROUND -
gaining speed from her forelegs and thighs.

She was known for her run, for being cheeky and fun and for her beautiful, straight shaped eyes.

The herd loved her talent,
strong legs and good balance;
they could see that her stride was unique.

So they booked her a place to
compete in a race that was called
the "THREE DESERT PEAKS".

There was no time for PLAY
as she trained every DAY
pushing on through the PAIN
and the SWEAT.

Many barks and loud moos
could be heard in the dunes
as the antelopes helped her get SET.

She kept herself
quiet and took care
of her diet,

carefully
grinding her food
up to eat.

Loose twigs and
small seeds, rough
grass and thin LEAVES

were enjoyed
as her
energy TREATS!

The time was now here
for the race of the year -
a spectacle not to be MISSED.

All those who took part
were able and smart;
twenty names were down
on the LIST.

With FIRE in their EYES
they were keen for first PRIZE,
not content to come second
or third.

But they secretly knew it was just the 'Top Two' who could beat this young doe in the herd.

The leopard's large stride was rapid and wide;
he was desperate to be the race WINNER.

The jackal had PACE and was up for the CHASE;

he could win and be back home for DINNER!

Pulled tight on the slope was
the starting line rope with
the twenty all ready to go.

"On your
marks,"

was announced
and off they all bounced.
The crowd was in for a show!

Chasing up the first peak they raced CHEEK to CHEEK;
they pounded the same on the next.

Then something went wrong. The doe was not strong;
she tripped, and fell down on her neck.

In a flash the race changed
and a look was exchanged:
the 'Top Two' had a
chance to be FIRST.

But they stopped
on the TRACK
and made their
way BACK - the
poor doe was in
need of a NURSE.

They came to her side and gave her a ride,
even though she was favourite to WIN.

With the doe limp and WEAK,
they climbed the last PEAK.
Together they both walked her IN.

The crowd could all see
they came in as a three
and chanted across
the red sand -

"Kindness means more
than winning for sure.
Thanks a lot for your
big helping hand."

Clare
Luther

She studied Occupational Therapy at
Oxford Brookes University. She worked as
an Occupational Therapist and Life
Coach, in both the public and private
sector, until 2013. Clare now has a diverse
work life where she continues to use her
skills in a variety of settings. She has
held a passion for writing poetry since
her teenage years. She lives in London
with her husband and two children.

Maria
Floyd

She studied Fine Art and History of Art
at Goldsmiths' College, London and is a
successful painter and illustrator. She
has held several exhibitions of her work
in the UK and divides her time between
Somerset and North Cornwall. She lives
with her husband and three children.